Theory of Music Grade 5
May 2016

CO

Your full name (as on appointment form). Please use BLOCK CAPITALS.

Your signature

Registration number

Centre

Instructions to Candidates

1. The time allowed for answering this paper is **three (3) hours.**
2. Fill in your name and the registration number printed on your appointment form in the appropriate spaces on this paper, and on any other sheets that you use.
3. **Do not open this paper until you are told to do so.**
4. This paper contains **seven (7) sections** and you should answer all of them.
5. Read each question carefully before answering it. Your answers must be written legibly in the spaces provided.
6. You are reminded that you are bound by the regulations for written exams displayed at the exam centre and listed on page 4 of the current edition of the written exams syllabus. In particular, you are reminded that you are not allowed to bring books, music or papers into the exam room. Bags must be left at the back of the room under the supervision of the invigilator.
7. If you leave the exam room you will not be allowed to return.

Examiner's use only:

1 (10)	
2 (15)	
3 (10)	
4 (15)	
5 (15)	
6 (15)	
7 (20)	
Total	

(A-05)

Section 1 (10 marks)

Boxes for examiner' use only

Put a tick (✓) in the box next to the correct answer.

Example

Name this note:

A ☐   D ☐   C ☑

This shows that you think **C** is the correct answer.

1.1   Name the circled note:

C ☐   B♮ ☐   E♮ ☐   ☐

1.2   Which is the correct time signature?

$\frac{9}{4}$ ☐ $\frac{7}{8}$ ☐ $\frac{12}{8}$ ☐   ☐

1.3   Which rest should be put below the asterisk (*) to complete the bar?

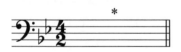

𝄽 ☐   𝄼 ☐   𝄻 ☐   ☐

1.4   Which note is the enharmonic equivalent of this note?

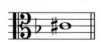

C ☐   D♭ ☐   D♯ ☐   ☐

1.5   Which note is the supertonic of the minor key shown by this key signature?

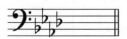

B♭ ☐   G♮ ☐   G ☐   ☐

Put a tick (✓) in the box next to the correct answer.

1.6 The correct name for the following broken chord is:

chord **I** in G major ☐
chord **V** in G major ☐
chord **i** in B minor ☐

☐

1.7 Name this cadence:

plagal cadence in B♭ major ☐
plagal cadence in G minor ☐
perfect cadence in G minor ☐

☐

1.8 Which Roman numeral fits below this subdominant triad?

IV ☐   **iv** ☐   **ii** ☐

☐

1.9 ⌇ means:

quickly spread out the notes of a chord ☐
play without the pedal ☐
shake ☐

☐

1.10 The interval of a major 3rd when inverted becomes:

a major 7th ☐
a minor 6th ☐
a perfect 4th ☐

☐

Section 2 (15 marks)

2.1   Write a one-octave G pentatonic major scale in minims, ascending then descending.

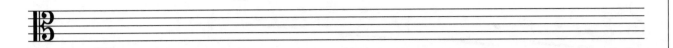

2.2   Write the key signature of the key shown. Then write its one-octave arpeggio in the rhythm
given below.

Db major, going down then up

Section 3 (10 marks)

3.1   Circle five different mistakes in the following music, then write it out correctly.

legato

Section 4 (15 marks)

4.1   Transpose this melody up a perfect 4th. Use a key signature.

Dubois

Section 5 (15 marks)

5.1   Using minims, write out 4-part chords for SATB using the chords shown by the Roman numerals below.

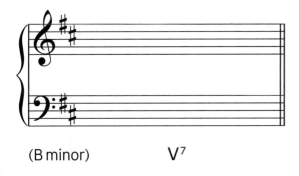

(B minor)   V⁷

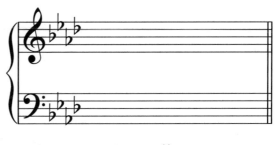

(A♭ major)   iic

Section 6 (15 marks)

6.1   Use notes from each chord shown by the chord symbols to write a tune above the bass line. Decorate your tune (eg with passing notes) once you have the main harmony notes in place.

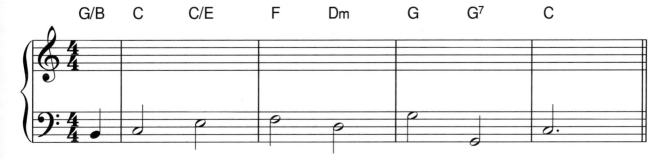

Section 7 (20 marks)

Look at the following piece and answer the questions opposite.

Folk song

2. And one of those ships was Noah's old Ark,
   And covered all over with hickory bark.
3. They filled up the seams with oakum pitch.
4. And Noah of old com-manded this Ark.

7.1 In which key is this song?_____

7.2 In what form is this song composed? _____

7.3 What does $\frac{6}{8}$ mean?_____

7.4 Does the song start on an anacrusis? _____

7.5 Circle an unaccented passing note in bar 2 (vocal part).

7.6 Write appropriate Roman numerals below the last two chords of the first phrase (piano part, bar 2).

7.7 Name the cadence formed by these two chords._____

7.8 Circle a dominant 7th chord.

7.9 Name the interval between the two notes marked with asterisks (*) in bar 4 (vocal part).

_____

7.10 Re-write the left-hand part of bar 7 in the tenor clef. Remember to use a key signature.

Theory of Music Grade 5
November 2016

TRINITY
COLLEGE LONDON

Your full name (as on appointment form). Please use BLOCK CAPITALS.

Your signature

Registration number

Centre

Instructions to Candidates

1. The time allowed for answering this paper is **three (3) hours**.
2. Fill in your name and the registration number printed on your appointment form in the appropriate spaces on this paper, and on any other sheets that you use.
3. **Do not open this paper until you are told to do so.**
4. This paper contains **seven (7) sections** and you should answer all of them.
5. Read each question carefully before answering it. Your answers must be written legibly in the spaces provided.
6. You are reminded that you are bound by the regulations for written exams displayed at the exam centre and listed on page 4 of the current edition of the written exams syllabus. In particular, you are reminded that you are not allowed to bring books, music or papers into the exam room. Bags must be left at the back of the room under the supervision of the invigilator.
7. If you leave the exam room you will not be allowed to return.

Examiner's use only:

1 (10)	
2 (15)	
3 (10)	
4 (15)	
5 (15)	
6 (15)	
7 (20)	
Total	

(C-05)

Section 1 (10 marks)

Put a tick (✓) in the box next to the correct answer.

Example

Name this note:

A ☐   D ☐   C ☑

This shows that you think **C** is the correct answer.

1.1   Name the circled note:

F# ☐   G# ☐   A# ☐   ☐

1.2   Which is the correct grouping of main beats in this bar?

3, 4 ☐   4, 1, 2 ☐   4, 3 ☐   ☐

1.3   Which note is the enharmonic equivalent of this note?

D♭ ☐   E♭ ☐   C× ☐   ☐

1.4   Which is the correct time signature?

$\frac{2}{4}$ ☐ $\frac{3}{8}$ ☐ $\frac{5}{8}$ ☐   ☐

1.5   What does *con forza* mean?   With fire ☐   Agitated ☐   With force ☐   ☐

Put a tick (✓) in the box next to the correct answer.

1.6   Which note is the supertonic of the minor key shown by this key signature?

Bb ☐   Ab ☐   C ☐   ☐

1.7   Which Roman numeral fits below this subdominant triad?

IV ☐   iv ☐   ii ☐   ☐

1.8   Which of these ornaments should be played as follows?

   ☐

1.9   Name the chord progression that makes this imperfect cadence in A major.

I-V ☐   i-v ☐   I-v ☐   ☐

1.10   Which instrument is **not** a member of the woodwind family?

Flute ☐
French horn ☐
Oboe ☐

          ☐

Please turn over for Section 2

Section 2 (15 marks)

Boxes for examiner use only

2.1   Write a one-octave G♯ melodic minor scale in minims, descending then ascending. Use the correct key signature.

2.2   Write the key signature of the key shown. Then write its one-octave arpeggio in the rhythm given below.

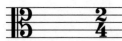

E major, descending then ascending

Section 3 (10 marks)

3.1   Circle five different mistakes in the following music, then write it out correctly.

4

Section 4 (15 marks)

4.1 Transpose this melody up a minor 3rd. Use a key signature.

Wilm

Section 5 (15 marks)

5.1 Using crotchets, write out 4-part chords for SATB using the chords shown by the Roman numerals below.

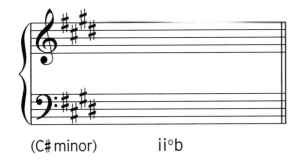

(C# minor)   ii°b

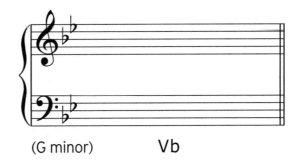

(G minor)   Vb

Section 6 (15 marks)

6.1 Use notes from the chords shown by the Roman numerals to write a tune above the bass line. Decorate your tune (eg with passing notes) once you have the main harmony notes in place.

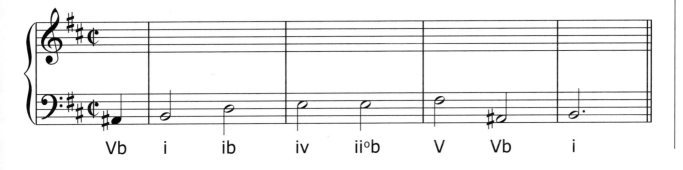

Vb   i   ib   iv   ii°b   V   Vb   i

Section 7 (20 marks)

Look at the following piece and answer the questions opposite.

Karganov

7.1   In which key is this piece? _____

7.2   Circle a first inversion dominant 7th chord in this key.

7.3   Name the interval between the two notes marked with asterisks (*) in bar 4 (LH).

_____

7.4   To which related key does the music modulate in bars 8 and 9? _____

7.5   What does **Allegro marziale** mean? _____

7.6   Circle an unaccented passing note in bar 14 (RH)._____

7.7   Write a Roman numeral below the third beat of bar 5.

7.8   Bracket (⊓) each step of the sequence in bars 6–7 (bass stave).

7.9   Name a string instrument which could play the melody on the bass stave of bars 2–9.

_____

7.10   Re-write the bass part in bar 9 in the tenor clef. Remember to use a key signature.